ACCOMPANIST EDITION

THE COMPLETE
CHORAL WARM-UP
SEQUENCES

Other publications by James Jordan relating to this volume:

Inside the Choral Rehearsal
G-9293

The Anatomy of Tone
G-9421

The Choral Warm-Up
G-6397

The Choral Warm-Up
Teaching and Rehearsal Cards
G-6397I

The Core Vocal Exercises
Accompanist Supplement with CD
G-6397A

Discovering Chant
G-8812

Ear Training Immersion Exercises for Choirs
G-6429

The Musician's Breath
G-7955

ACCOMPANIST EDITION

THE COMPLETE CHORAL WARM-UP SEQUENCES

A COMPANION TO
THE CHORAL WARM-UP
INSIDE THE CHORAL REHEARSAL
THE ANATOMY OF TONE

James Jordan
Jesse Borower

Brian Sengdala
Editor

Contributors:
Corey Everly and Marilyn Shenenberger
&
Asherah Capellaro, Megan Coiley, Paul Georgeson
Daegun Ha, Lucy Hole, Alkistis Karatzis, Colton Martin
Jacob Nelson, Sunny Park, Alexander Rosa

GIA Publications, Inc.
Chicago

Layout Design: Jesse Borower
Art Direction: Martha Chlipala
G-9543A
ISBN: 978-1-62277-256-8

Copyright © 2018 GIA Publications, Inc.
7404 S. Mason Avenue, Chicago, Illinois 60638
www.giamusic.com

CONTENTS

The Core Vocal Exercises

Aural Immersion Exercises

THE CORE VOCAL EXERCISES

from *The Choral Warm-Up: Core Vocal Exercises* (GIA, 2004)

Recordings of accompaniments for these exercises are available for download at giamusic.com/ccws

Note: The Core Vocal Exercises selected for use in this book are available in full in a separate accompanist edition (G-6397A).

INTRODUCTION

Marilyn Shenenberger

In serving as accompanist for the Westminster Chapel Choir, I endeavored to provide accompaniments for the warm-ups that supplied a rich harmonic canvas while supporting the pedagogical objectives of the exercises. It is imperative that these exercises be played with nuance, line, and rhythmic integrity. Well-harmonized exercises enrich the aural vocabularies of each singer; properly voiced accompaniments encourage supported, seated singing; and rhythmically secure accompaniments have the ability to provide a healthy rhythmic impetus that can assist with the singing of forward-moving and energized musical line. In addition, the accompaniment can support the intonation of the choir by incorporating the dominant ostinato principles that are advocated in both publications, *Choral Ensemble Intonation* and *Ear Training Immersion Exercises for Choirs*. Exercises that are voiced with psychological forethought concerning how to guide the choir to listen can provide efficient musical instruction.

By writing out these exercises, we are hoping to take the mystery out of choral warm-ups so a quality warm-up can be a consistent beginning for every rehearsal. By having the notated accompaniments, the accompanist is free to listen more and think less about the theory behind the keyboard improvisation. When a substitute accompanist was needed for Dr. Jordan's Chapel Choir, we would ask one of the students to play the rehearsal. Their biggest apprehension was that of improvising the accompaniment while modulating upward by half steps—and not in their wildest dreams had they ever contemplated modulating downward by half steps! The modulations are, therefore, written out for the accompanist, and they should be practiced by all your accompanists so they sound effortless in the choral rehearsal. All modulations are through the dominant of the new key, or by way of a diminished seventh chord. A consistent accompaniment is of great assistance to the conductor and is necessary in providing stability for the beginning of each rehearsal.

The accompanist is a collaborative artist with the conductor and, in many ways, an equal partner in the pedagogical process of teaching a choir. The singers will emulate the musicianship of their director. An accompanist who plays with nuance, musical understanding, a listening ear, and sensitivity to the director's interpretation is the best resource a conductor can have to ensure a high standard of musicality within the choir. While the accompanist is wordless in the rehearsal, a skilled accompanist can affect the musical line, expressivity, and musical awareness, in addition to intonation and rhythmic acuity, simply through the music they provide.

If the accompanist has an understanding of how the choir learns and how they hear, that person can provide constant and ongoing non-verbal musical instruction to the choir. Of course, this can only be effective if the choir is encouraged to listen constantly to the keyboard and if the accompanist listens for what support the choir needs. Sometimes LESS is MORE. In other words, the accompanist should provide only what is necessary for the choir to be successful. With a new exercise or new piece of music, it is often necessary to play what the choir is to sing, but accompanists often make the mistake of playing that long after the choir can and should be singing it on their own. In the warm-up exercises, the choir sings the same two- or four-measure phrases one or more times. When the exercise is brand new, it should be presented vocally by the director. It may then be necessary for the accompanist to play the choir's melodic line in the right hand through two or three keys at most and then play only the written accompaniment unless the choir is faltering with the melody.

The voicing of the specific accompaniments was done with this pedagogical objective in mind. Range extension exercises must provide a strong bass that simulates the support needed for singing in the upper register. Sostenuto or line exercises with repeated tones (which will tend to go flat) need to incorporate the fifth played an octave above what the choir sings, which will give the singers the aural anchor they need to sing in tune. Slow exercises should include subdivision in the accompaniment so the singers feel the pulsing necessary to keep the line moving forward. Repetitive interval exercises require a directional line in the accompaniment that infuses the exercise with tension toward the resolution. Exercises that incorporate rests need an accompaniment that instills a sense of direction so the rests are active rests, not inactive, which will cause "off-the-breath" singing. The needs of the singers are the same whether the choir is small or large, although the volume and intensity of the accompaniment will vary in proportion to the size of the choir. Boychoirs and all girl choruses will need a softer touch on the marcato and martellato exercises.

Basic Rules for Accompanists

1. **Be musical!** Not all notes are created equal! The traditional piano student begins by learning the notes, finding the notes with facility, following the printed dynamics, and working the selection up to tempo. The instructor is usually the advisor to the nuances that are hidden within the blueprint of the printed page, but are necessary to make the performance of the piece a musical experience for the performer as well as the listener. We are asking the accompanist to go beyond the traditional "piano player" role and become a pianist. They need to know how to bring out the music without the presence of their piano teacher, as we often ask them to demonstrate it for the whole choir! If your accompanists are piano players rather than pianists, you will need to work with them outside of the rehearsal to help them read more than the notes to make the music come alive.

2. **Listen at all times.** The accompanist should strive to listen at all times to the choir. By constantly listening, the accompanist will hear when singers are hesitant, are unsure of the pitch, or have misheard the pitch, all of which indicate the need for the part to be reinforced.

3. **Play the exercises in a consistent tempo.** These exercises should be performed in the same tempo from the beginning to the end, with a slight ritardando possible nearing the final resolution. While it is the choir's responsibility to maintain tempo, the accompanist can certainly influence the maintenance of tempo by keeping a rock solid beat without playing metronomically. ANY DISRUPTION OF TEMPO UPSETS THE SINGERS' BREATHING PROCESS. Once the breathing process is upset, a process that is controlled by exact and consistent tempo, other vocal problems will appear. Among the resultant problems, "off-the-breath" singing and high larynx are the most serious. Many accompaniments include subdivisions of the macro beat the choir is singing for this very reason.

4. **Physically breathe with the conductor on the preparatory beat.** This beat provides far more than tempo. It informs the accompanist and singers of the effect of the piece: the tone color and the dynamics.

5. **Think about the color of the exercises.** The touch of the pianist determines whether the sound will be warm, crisp, brittle, expansive, tentative, harsh, etc. This directly affects the choir's perception of the piece and the color they will sing. One well-played section of a piece can convey more information than a ten-minute explanation. Directors should rehearse with the accompanists before the rehearsal to be sure the information conveyed is what is desired, and be vigilant that the quality of tone played continually reflects the tone quality desired in the ensemble!

6. **Observe pedaling as indicated.** Close observance of pedaling is important so the exercises have rhythmic and acoustic clarity.

7. **Know what to supply in the accompaniment when the choir BEGINS to sing out of tune.** If the intonation begins to slip, the accompanist should play the fifth an octave above the choir. This may be done by oscillating between the fifth and the root, using the fifth and root in an Alberti bass pattern above the choir, or simply adding the fifth in octaves on beats 2 and 4. The piece will determine which pattern fits best, as well as determining whether the root is the resting tone of the passage or the dominant. In the case of chromatic passages, it may be necessary to change the anchor tones often.

8. **Encourage vocal independence.** Voice parts will need to be played initially but should be left out as soon as the singers are confident. At this time, the accompanist should play aural anchors while listening for parts that need occasional assistance. If the accompaniment provides harmonic information apart from doubling the voice parts, it may be helpful for the choir to hear it. If, however, it is discordant, allow the choir to become more familiar with their parts before adding the accompaniment.

9. **Surround your singers with quality sound.** The timbre and intonation of the piano will directly influence the sound of the choir. Consequently, it behooves any choir to have the finest piano in their rehearsal room—and a piano that is in tune! The accompanist should check the piano and, if necessary, avoid playing notes that are seriously out of tune. This may mean playing one hand in a different octave for a week until the piano can be tuned. Be vigilant that the quality of tone being played directly reflects the tone quality desired in the ensemble!

Finally, and perhaps most importantly, the exercises should be played in such a way that evokes good singing and is pleasurable for the singers no matter how often they are sung. And above all, they must ensure that all sounds made during the rehearsal, no matter how simple the melodic idea, are at all times musical and expressive.

#1
Legato; Line

Acc. Marilyn Shenenberger

#2
Repeated Tone with
Crescendo and Decrescendo

Acc. Marilyn Shenenberger

#3
Maintain Spacious, High, and Forward
in Low Register

Acc. Marilyn Shenenberger

#4
Legato at Slow Tempo

Acc. Marilyn Shenenberger

This page intentionally left blank.

#5
Singing on Breath Through
Moving Eighth Notes

Acc. Marilyn Shenenberger

Dee dee dee   dee dee dee

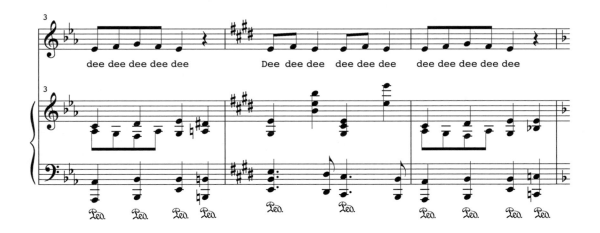

dee dee dee dee dee   Dee dee dee   dee dee dee   dee dee dee dee dee

#6
Range Consistency
with Downward Leaps

Acc. Marilyn Shenenberger

#7
Range Extension Downwards

Acc. Marilyn Shenenberger

#8
Range Extension Downwards

Acc. Marilyn Shenenberger

Dee dee dee   dee dee dee dee dee   dee dee dee dee dee dee dee dee dee

Dee dee dee   dee dee dee dee dee   dee dee dee dee dee dee dee dee dee

#9
Range Extension Upward
and Maintaining On-the-Breath Singing

Acc. Marilyn Shenenberger

This page intentionally left blank.

#10
Creating Space for Ascending Line

Acc. Marilyn Shenenberger

#11
Martellato Range Extension Downwards

Acc. Marilyn Shenenberger

#12
Marcato;
Upward Leaps on the Breath

Acc. Marilyn Shenenberger

#13
Upward Leaps on the Breath,
with Line; Listening

Acc. Marilyn Shenenberger

This page intentionally left blank.

#14
Range Extension Upward

Acc. Marilyn Shenenberger

This page intentionally left blank.

#15
Range Consistency
with Upward and Downward Leaps

Acc. Marilyn Shenenberger

#16
Upward Leaps on the Breath;
with Line

Acc. Marilyn Shenenberger

#17
Making Space on Upward Leap;
Vowel Modification

Acc. Marilyn Shenenberger

#18
Range Extension

Acc. Marilyn Shenenberger

#19
Martellato

Acc. Marilyn Shenenberger

#20
Range Extension

Acc. Marilyn Shenenberger

AURAL IMMERSION EXERCISES

from *Ear Training Immersion Exercises for Choirs* (GIA, 2004)

> Recordings of accompaniments for these exercises are available for download at giamusic.com/ccws

Note: The use of the Aural Immersion Exercises are most effective if the singers are using the Ensemble Editions (G-6429A).

INTRODUCTION

Marilyn Shenenberger

There are two strategies for the use of these materials, both equally acceptable and pedagogically sound. The first is to use these exercises as a sequential method of teaching aural familiarity with all the modes. The materials presented in full in *Ear Training Immersion Exercises for Choirs* are in the order of easiest to hear to most difficult to hear based upon the research of Edwin Gordon. If one is providing aural training for an ensemble or one has the rehearsal time, these materials should be presented as they are in that volume, with all the exercises being sung as stated in the instructions to provide a comprehensive aural introduction to all the modes.

The second way (the way that this book seeks to serve) is to extract the section of exercises needed for the mode of the piece that is being introduced or taught in a particular rehearsal. That is, if a choral work in Lydian is to be rehearsed that day, then the instructor should insert the exercises from the Lydian section of the text at the end of the choral warm-up. While most situations will not allow for a performance of all the exercises in that section, one should strive to at least perform the intonation, interval, and warm-up exercises for that particular mode. Over a number of rehearsals, it is best if the harmonized intonation is performed in that mode in each rehearsal.

If several pieces are to be rehearsed in a single rehearsal, then a change of mode in the rehearsal MUST be preceded with an "aural clearing of the air." That is, the aural environment must be reset for the choir. If the instructor does not do this, one can assume that rather than hearing the piece in the mode, they will default to trying to associate and tune the mode with what is most familiar to them: major.

A Note Concerning Tuned Pianos

Special attention must be paid to the maintenance of piano tuning. Because of the volatility of a singer's ears at this stage of development, the piano used to accompany the choir must be in tune. If it is not possible to maintain an acoustic piano in such a fashion, then an electronic instrument should be employed. Recordings are available for download if an electronic instrument is not available. Remember that intonation is a learned skill. If inaccurate pitch surrounds singers, then that is what they will learn to accept as the norm.

The Keyboard Accompaniments in This Volume

The accompaniments in this volume must be played exactly as notated. Omission of parts or re-harmonization of these exercises will diminish the potency of the exercises. Special care must be taken to observe this rule in all the exercises, but especially in the modal exercises.

Cautionary note: If ensembles have difficulty performing any of the tasks requested in this volume, it is recommended that pattern training be undertaken as detailed by Edwin Gordon in the *Jump Right In Music Series*. An inability to perform the musical tasks in this volume is indicative that there is not sufficient aural readiness for the singer to hear and musically understand what he/she is hearing. Pattern training should be undertaken emphasizing the aural/oral level of learning and the verbal association level of learning. The tonalities of major, minor, Mixolydian, and Dorian should be explored using these materials. And, as was stated earlier, none of these materials should be used unless a standardized measure of music aptitude has been administered.

General Teaching Procedure

1. Make certain students notice in their performance edition the tonality they are about to sing and its construction.

2. At this point, it may be helpful to remind singers to "listen to everyone else except themselves" to promote aware audiation.

3. All exercises should be sung first on neutral syllables. For legato passages, "noo" is the preferred syllable; however, "nee" should be used for more accurate pitch. For non-legato passages, "doo" is the syllable of choice. Never use any other syllables!

4. After one or two repetitions with neutral syllables, move to solfege syllables (as suggested in *Choral Ensemble Intonation*). Make certain solfege syllables are sung with sufficient vowel closure to ensure accurate pitch via a good pitch core.

5. Never sing the exercises without the accompaniments. Be certain to include the dominant function ostinato as notated in the examples!

6. Return to neutral syllable when intonation has stabilized to make certain there is sufficient musical line.

7. Begin each exercise with a rhythmic breath in the value of the "beat" or "pulse" of the piece. Breathe in the unit of the beat that you would walk to in performing the piece.

Specific Teaching Procedures

Extended Intonation Exercises for Each Tonality:

1. Make certain students notice the modality of the scale through either your announcement or their reading of the information at the top of the score.

2. Sing the exercise first on neutral syllable.

3. Proceed to solfege syllables as printed. Make sure vowels are adequately closed to ensure accurate pitch.

4. Use pointing if necessary (as demonstrated on the *Choral Ensemble Intonation* video).

Interval Exercises:

These exercises are important to establish accurate intonation within the tonality the choir is singing. Interval exercises should ONLY be performed after an intonation exercise has been sung.

1. Listen to the voice part played with the accompaniment, either by the accompanist or with the recording.

2. Sing the exercise in unison with solfege syllables.

3. Make certain the aural anchors in the accompaniment are supplied in ALL readings of the exercises.

4. On exercises that use leaps, make certain to minimize glissando by asking the choir to point on the attack of each note.

5. Make certain to reinforce on repetitions of the exercise having the choir listen to the keyboard part more than they listen to themselves.

Harmonic Minor Intervals with Aural Anchors

Do is F; the Resting Tone is D (La)

Aural anchors should be played in addition to the piano chords

Harmonic Minor Tuning Warm-Up I

Do is F; the Resting Tone is D (La)

Mixolydian Intervals

Do is G; the Resting Tone is D (Sol)

Mixolydian Tuning Warm-Up I

Do is G; the Resting Tone is D (Sol)

Dorian Intervals

Do is C; the Resting Tone is D (Re)

_____ indicates the middle, or Sostenuto, pedal is to be used with the left foot.

℘ℯ𝒹. below indicates that the Damper pedal should be used simultaneously, although it changes with more frequency than the Sostenuto pedal.

D Dorian Tuning Warm-Up I

Do is C; the Resting Tone is D (Re)

Lydian Intervals

Do is A; the Resting Tone is D (Fa)

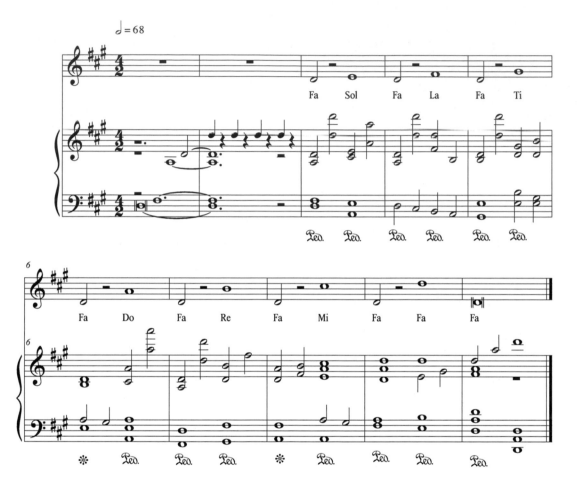

Lydian Tuning Warm-Up I

Do is A; the Resting Tone is D (Fa)

Phrygian Intervals

Do is B-flat; the Resting Tone is D (Mi)

_____ indicates the middle, or Sostenuto, pedal is to be used with the left foot.

℗ℯ𝒹. below indicates that the Damper pedal should be used simultaneously,
although it changes with more frequency than the Sostenuto pedal.

Phrygian Tuning Warm-Up II

Do is B-flat the Resting Tone is D (Mi)

Aeolian Intervals

Do is F; the Resting Tone is D (La)

Aeolian Tuning Warm-Up I

Do is F; the Resting Tone Is D (La)

Damper Pedal should be changed with every left hand chord.

Locrian Intervals

Do is E-flat; the Resting Tone is D (Ti)

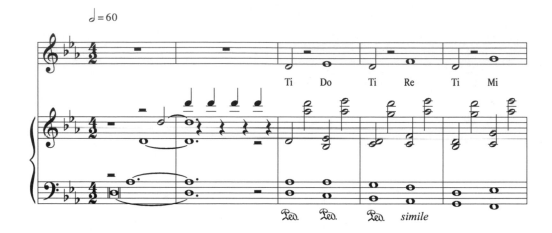

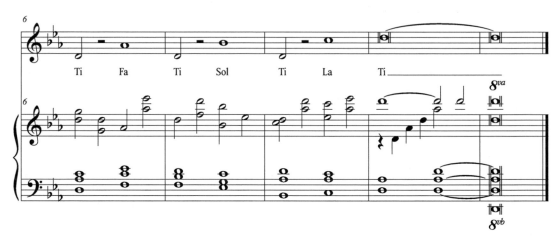

Locrian Tuning Warm-Up II

Do is E-flat; the Resting Tone is D (Ti)

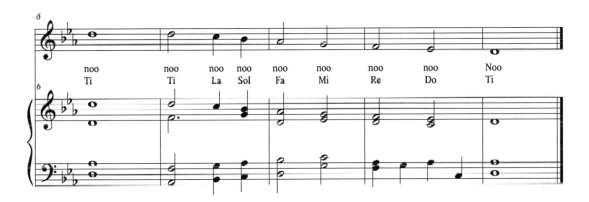